THiS jOURNAL BELONGS TO

_____

introduction

When you are drawn to Rumi, you are being drawn into a passionate love affair with the sacred, the divine, the spiritual, and the earthly. In the mystical and poetic world of Rumi, there is no separation between life on earth and in heaven. There is only the invitation to realise the presence of divine love in all things, in all experiences, lying in wait for our souls, waiting to pounce upon us when we least expect it, with loving playfulness and startling truth.

It is my belief that Rumi is a spiritual guide for the human collective at this time. His teachings are not about religion or even about philosophy, they entreat us into an experience of the Divine as our great beloved, our friend, our encourager, our challenger (to bring the best out in us) and the great one into whom we can surrender and discover more wonder, joy and passion than we have ever known.

Rumi brings out the optimist, the one who is not afraid to be foolish, the one who is therefore courageous and willing to live life and not hide away behind controlling perfectionism. When I contemplate Rumi, I imagine our souls as being ravished by the Divine. We could worry that our hair is out of place and turn the lights off and hide beneath a sheet, not making a sound. Or we could open our souls up to the Divine, willing to have our hair and our souls divinely dishevelled, trusting there is only love in the exchange, and nothing to fear.

I remember hearing a story about a man who was having a really difficult day. He was dumped by his business partners quite out of the blue, and came home that evening to be dumped by his wife, too. It was not the way he saw his day progressing when he woke up that morning! However, it was so profoundly shocking that he had a sudden thought. Only the Divine could mess up his life with so much power and precision in such an instant way! So instead of worrying, he decided to trust that the Divine was up to something. As it turned out, his intuition was correct and many changes that brought greater happiness to all involved unfolded through his trusting attitude. You could say that he wasn't afraid when the Divine was pulling at his soul shirt and passionately messing up his hair.

Rumi's mystical poetry is an encouragement towards unconditional trust because he believes in the unconditional love that the Divine has for us, and that we are deep within. In a world that is still so often dominated by fear-based, status-oriented, control-driven attitudes, his active encouragement to surrender and seek the deeper meaning meaning of our life experience is a welcome relief. Even on the path of spiritual healing and self-improvement we need to take care. Rumi reminds us that all life experiences are valuable, and that becoming a better person is not necessarily the point of the path at all. Through his guiding light we find permission to be ourselves – our human, messy, soulful and sometimes downright confused or bewildered selves.

If we are in love with the Divine, passionate about spirit, then we are going to be contemplating a vast intelligence that we cannot possibly understand. That means we are going to be scratching our heads a lot and wondering what the Universe is up to! That's fine. In fact, it's important. It's part of how we can express our devotion – to just be in awe and say wow, because we saw a polka-dotted bee for the first time (it's called a domino cuckoo bee, by the way) or because there was an incredible lunar eclipse that made the moon look like a blood-red celestial omen. It also means that when things seem to be falling apart around our ears, we can also say wow, and remain willing to participate in this strangely beautiful mystery that we know as life.

Rumi often speaks of intoxication as an analogy for how we feel when we are drunk on divine bliss. If you've ever had this experience yourself, you'll know that is exactly how it feels – like being happily drunk (but with a healthier liver the next morning). There are times when, in our intention to make progress in our lives, even on our spiritual or self-healing path, we can forget how important it is to have fun, to enjoy the occasional ridiculousness of life, to laugh at a volume that is not appropriate (writing that just made me snort-laugh SO loudly) and basically let go and feel alive.

Rumi helps us keep a check on our seriousness so that it is useful but not constraining to the wild misfit within that needs to be let out to play from time to time. That part of us understands that sometimes giggling hysterically, to the point that you cannot do anything else, may well be the best medicine for what ails the mind. This is the part of us that is not afraid to mess up and therefore is willing to take chances in life. This is the sort of soul that the Universe loves to play with, to lead on adventures, to share great mysteries and insights with … that open, curious, sense-of-humour-intact being is a magnet for divine blessing and mystical experience.

Rumi helps us connect with this cheeky and curious consciousness within. He helps us remember that love is a festival, a celebration, an invitation to the greatest divine party ever. You may well be swinging from a crystal chandelier, trying to fly, as the raucous evening progresses, but the Divine is not going to punish you for it. Instead you'll just be granted wings to help you fulfil your heart's desire for lift off.

When you are ready to deepen your journey with Rumi, it's time to give up being the warrior and embrace being the lover and the beloved. It's time to experience your life not as an endless obstacle course to be navigated, or battle to be won, but rather as a great big playground and sumptuous banquet where you get to experience as much as your soul is hungry for – and then some – whilst running wild with other souls, recognising that the same divine light that you love so much also burns in you and in all beings.

It is also a time when you can be sure that your soul is asking you to give up on the way you have related to the Universe and open yourself to a more radically unconditional form of trust. It is advanced spiritual training to learn how to be at peace no matter what is unfolding in your life. When you are going through big growth spurts, it's not necessarily easy to accept the darkness and pain that can arise as part of that process, even if you know at a deeper level that it will ultimately bring you greater light, happiness and peace in time. Rumi doesn't want us to wait until later to feel trust and love for the Universe, he wants us to live it now—in the dark night of the soul and in the bright light of a breakthrough into greater divine connection. He reminds us that it is all part of the workings—mysterious as they are—of a greater divine love in our lives.

In a way this lets us off the hook of the misconception that if something is not flowing in our lives, we must be doing something wrong. Sometimes there is chaos because we are ready for something new and different, the old is dismantled so that the new can emerge. It's like a home renovation in the soul and in our lives—a mess, but worth it for the end result!

Rumi's guiding light helps us remember that night will turn into day, but we don't have to wait for that moment to feel hope and relief. Remembering that we are loved, that we can laugh, that we can recognise and embrace the silliness of our own antics, we can be human with all it entails, including vibrant creativity, profound wisdom and the ability to trip over the edge of a Turkish carpet at the precise moment we want to make a fabulous first impression. Rumi just shrugs his soul shoulders, beams at us with love in his eyes, and leans over to playfully tug at our nose. May his beautiful spirit free you from guilt, shame and fear, and empower you to live your life fully and freely, from the heart.

With love and blessings,

Alana

This ending comes as grace to free you from all that you have known, for what you have known is now too small for your soul.

There may be uncertainty and even insecurity. Yet you have a heart big enough to bear such growing pains. Your heart is even big enough to receive the joy that is lying in wait for you as you stumble across her in the course of your clumsy, inspired travails into new life.

The Divine is a relentless lover. It wants nothing less than your total being to be held in its embrace. Sometimes that means we will have to give up lesser loves for the greater lover—the divine one that calls us to remember our true nature.

Life supports all beings in their true nature. The birds are given air in which to fly, and fish are given water in which to swim. Each aspect of creation is given what it requires so it may become what it is meant to be ... for its unique destiny to be fulfilled.

We must dare to believe that we are not broken, that we are not inadequate or would be better off being like some other person, or adhering to some other person's view of how they think we should be! We must be brave enough not to believe in the layers of guilt and shame. We must be bold enough not to fear our passion.

A deep silence overcomes me, and I wonder why I ever thought to utter words.
— Rumi

At first, passionate purpose may be barely recognisable amongst all the 'shoulds', 'cannots' or 'must dos' of our lives. However, as we stay true to the path, that light will become unmistakably clear. Our passion will reveal itself to us, as essential as our breath!

If parts of your life are disassembling, or do not seem to be working out as you had planned, these are symptoms of a passionate revelation. Be curious and open to all that presents itself in the wake of the falling away.

The Divine is fierce, wild, inexplicable and demanding beyond all measure. It wants you. Completely. Utterly. Without condition. There will be times in your life—such as now—when something not worthy of you must be released. This allows the Divine to move closer and burn brighter within you.

At the height of summer, you cast aside the layers of clothing you require in the winter. This is natural. You do not think twice about it. As you approach the radiant sun of divinity, your emotional and psychological layers are to be shed too, for they are too heavy for the heat of the great spiritual sun.

Trust in your changing perspective and perceptions. Don't hold onto what you once believed or thought to be true. Allow yourself to be shown another version of events, another way of perceiving.

That which plagues you — whether it is something specific, a general nagging malaise or an anxiety you cannot quite pin down — is not as powerful as you fear. You are being given a grace, here and now, so that it may be overcome. Healing has been made possible through divine protection now.

Sometimes we just need permission to break down, to really let go, to come apart and be disassembled, so that we can break through, be lifted up, and come together in a new, more spiritually coherent and loving form.

Do not hold onto scraps for fear that the feast will be denied to you.
Use your nose! Smell the feast awaiting you!

Love, like life, flows through the heart. Feel the thrill of the flow and say nothing.
— Rumi

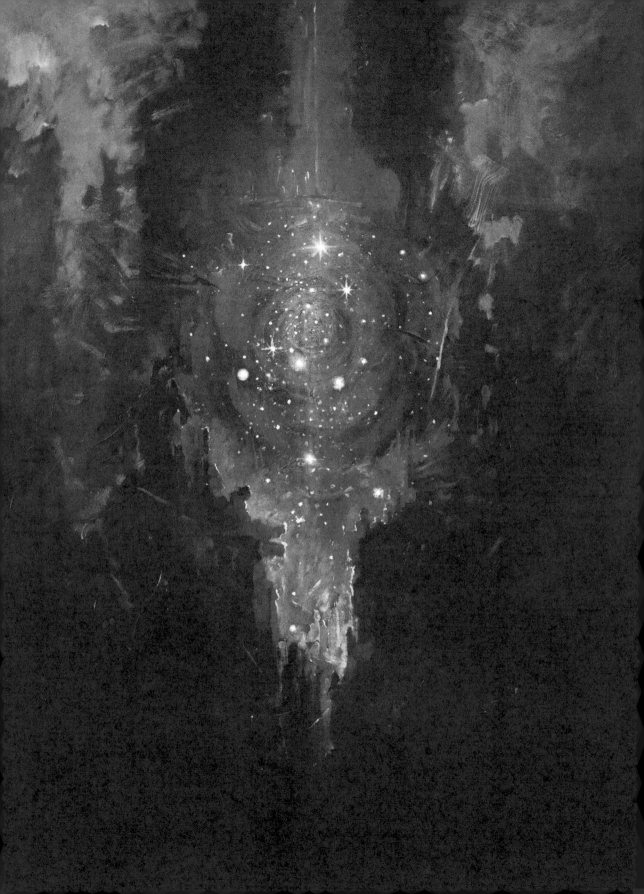

A (LOVING) PUSH FOR YOUR PASSIONATE PURPOSE

SPIRITUAL GUIDANCE

Plants are given the light of the open plains, or the darkness of the damp rainforest, depending on their needs for growth. Bees have wings that are very small, but powerful enough to move with such speed and rotation that their heavy bodies can fly. Each aspect of creation is given what it requires so it may become what it is meant to be, for its unique destiny to be fulfilled.

So it is with humanity. Each one of us has something in our hearts that means something to us. We would feel as though we were not alive without it. How could we have missed it all those years, perhaps all those lifetimes? It will seem so obvious then, burning so clear in our hearts that it cannot be more apparent, that we simply must live this desire, this passion, this purpose, or else spiritually perish into a shrivelled shell of a person, denying of life itself! No! That shall not be! Passion must and shall prevail.

You are strong enough to leave behind the need for external validation whilst you learn to validate yourself, unlearning the play-acting attempt to be a false self so that you can simply love and accept your real self.

SACRED HONOURING RITUAL

Say the following aloud: *Rumi, who loves me unconditionally, guardian of my heart, help me witness, receive and express the divine depths of my passionate purpose. With merciful grace, help me recognise my life purpose without doubt or fear. Help me realise that I have it within me to completely fulfil my divine destiny during this lifetime. So be it.*

Sit quietly and imagine or intend that energy from the universal heart of love is flowing in through the back of your heart and circulating between your belly and your heart. If it helps, you may like to place one hand on your heart, and one over your belly as you relax into that feeling of receiving healing divine energy.

Any misconceptions or obstructions can now flow easily out through the back of your heart as you are filled with new universal energies. Stay with this gentle process for as long as feels right for you.

When you are ready, find a comfortable position. Sense your grounded presence. Feel your own energy, your own being. This is the Universe playing at being you. It wants to be you. Accept this and make peace with yourself and the Universe. Trust in who you are. Trust in what you are becoming.

Don't be upset if you see the garden of the rebellious is greener.
— *Rumi*

Disorder is the ego perspective of higher order because its range of vision is too small, too limited. That is as it should be. The teacup is not made to hold the ocean, but a cup of tea! But when we imagine the cup of tea is preferable to the ocean, because it is more containable, how much we miss out on!

Why the frowning, the fear or the questioning? Let me share a sublime secret with you. Let me whisper it into your heart now. There is nothing to fear.

*No matter how dire circumstances may appear to be or despairing you may feel,
there is still an avenue through which fulfilment and resolution will be granted.*

The Divine keeps rigorous, flawless accounts. Therefore, nothing shall be left unaccounted for— not even that which seems to be outside divine attention and grace at this moment.

*When opening to receive more, one needs to empty out what has been, to allow for
a new influx of energy. It is not about having an exchange of equal measure,
for you will receive according to the great generosity of life itself. Thus, even more
shall be offered in compensation for what you are willing to release.*

Do not make yourself too small for what is now happening in your soul and in your life, by holding onto what you know when it is better to let go.

The soul hears a call from within, how long will you wander around?
Come back home. —— Rumi

I bow to this living, beating, loving heart of the Universe. It echoes throughout all of creation. Once, some time ago, I was deaf. I had not heard one true sound. Much noise, but no truth. I believed in many things not worth believing in. Now I know that belief in unworthy things—like fear and doubt—is lunacy. Even my loneliness became unconvincing to me.

I link my arm through yours and I urge you on. Let us run together and jump over the edge! No more half living for you and me. We will weep crystal clear tears and we will laugh with such joy that stars will burst forth, borne upon our exhalations. We will hear the beating of the cosmic heart pounding in our ears, and how we shall dance to it! That sacred intoxicating rhythm moves hips and hands and hearts, to raise the soul from slumber.

Divine love can be startling to the parts of you unused to such wild unconditional affection and rowdy playfulness. You may worry that this great love is not going to be careful enough with you. Fear not, love has its wisdom and its way. We shall become lost in its genius together.

More love is rushing towards you like a great cosmic tsunami. You will struggle with this blessing to the extent that you will attempt to hold onto what has been. So don't. Let go. Let it move you. You'll perhaps get some water up your nose, but nothing will come to you that you cannot handle.

All of creation is born from nothing. Out of endless silence and darkness, light emerges. What strange magic is this? We dance in the realm of the impossible made constantly possible, you and I. We are so engrossed in it, so familiar with it and yet blind to it, that the constant impossibilities happening in every moment fail to inspire us.

What are your biggest, boldest, most extraordinarily impossible dreams compared to the great impossibility of life itself? Ah, they are but tiny seeds in the Creator's masterful hand, being planted in the heavenly garden. Yes, they are being planted right now, for the moon tells us the time is right. Most tenderly shall they be watched over, nurtured into fullness according to the season.

We only limit what we believe to be possible by our lack of imagination! The Divine has recourse to all that is and all that is yet to be. Is there any limit to the resources of the heavens? No!

The Universe wants something to happen for you, something beautiful, something utterly improbable, and something perfect for your path, your own unique divine destiny. When your heart is much more powerful than your mind, you won't unintentionally block the incredible workings of divine grace.

What makes the moon melt its brilliance upon us? It is the fire of longing in the heart, and the love for the source of all beauty! — *Rumi*

A VITALITY BLESSING OF THE BLOOD ANGEL

SPIRITUAL GUIDANCE

You are being gifted more aliveness, more soul, more light. You are becoming more alive, open and vital. There will be more sunsets, to allow for the increase in your sunrises. This is about balance. The emptying out of what has been allows us to be receptive. The sunset makes way for a time of night – that might be the darkness of grief, or simply for the rest that is required to be ready for a new day. Being ready to embrace the beauty of the sunset, and the healing restorative power of the night, is essential for you to receive the new dawn being offered to your soul.

Why is this coming to you? You are ready for it. You have outgrown what has been and it cannot satisfy your soul anymore. A new vitality is ready to blossom in your soul. The Universe is giving you the blessing of whatever energy is required to expand into wherever life is leading you. All the Divine has instilled within your heart shall be financed with life force and energy, so it may be brought to fulfilment. This is the sacred contract of human life. The journey shall be taken by the soul, and there will be challenges, and yet what is required for divine fulfilment will be available to you.

SACRED HONOURING RITUAL

Perhaps there is something in your life that you would love to do, if only you had the energy or other resources to do it. This healing ritual is an affirmation of the Universe's desire and ability to support you with all that is needed to manifest your true heart's desires.

Imagine that your soul can have a conversation with the Universe. Let your soul ask the

Universe what it needs to release, and write the answer down, without thinking about it. Let your soul ask the Universe, "what do you want to bring to me for my highest good?" and write it down, without thinking about it.

Then say: *Blood Angel of unconditional life and divine love, bless me with the life force I need to attain my divine destiny. I open to your grace with perfect trust and perfect love. So be it.*

Everyone is dancing to the rhythm played by the tambourine of destiny! No one could dance without your beat! No one could move unless you move! The sound of the tambourine is hidden and yet the dance of life is visible! — Rumi

Thorns serve an essential purpose. I cannot begrudge them. I love the rose—and so I love what is necessary for her to be. Thus, I love the thorns too.

Those that dampen your spirits or drag you down are to be dispensed with—no matter what games of blame or manipulation they may play to keep you coming back for more. Turn towards those connections that feel nourishing to your soul, so you can share yourself without fear.

I see in you, a divine wild child and sacred heart. You have gumption! Chutzpah! Guts! You dare to love where others only see pain. You dare to believe that everything will somehow work out, where others see only what they judge to be wrong.

It is the divine rebel in you that refuses to surrender hope. Give up the fight perhaps, the battle that comes from a place of fear, but never give up your hope. That hope in your heart, that optimism and patience that love will grow, creates a light within you that helps the world see through darkness.

The stars do appear to shine brighter at night, beloved, so don't become consumed by your nightmares. They will pass with the coming dawn, you'll see.

Gently lay to rest the suffering that has been—perhaps because of what you have labelled as the failure, the doubt, the losses and setbacks. They are so little in the greater scheme of you. Put them aside; allow them to rot and become fertiliser for life, but do not try to keep them alive beyond their earthly expiry date.

A prayer for releasing the past: With deep soul-daring, I choose to say thank you and goodbye to my past. What has been is no longer to be. I am at peace with this, for what has been is nothing more than fertiliser for life to flourish now. With complete forgiveness and acceptance, I let go.

A prayer of invitation for the future: I invite in life. I invite in love. I invite in what is required for my own spiritual success and thriving divinity. Through unconditional love and divine mercy, through the guiding spirit of my soul brother, Rumi, so be it.

A prayer for the present moment: In this present moment, life thrives. It is within this thriving grace that I now choose to place my consciousness. I am an angel ablaze. I trust in the benevolent divinity guiding my way.

Love is my medicine. Intelligent medicine. It takes death and makes it a
passageway into greater life. What genius is this? A genius that will render
anything and everything as a pathway to life.

I have found a bench upon which we may be seated. Nay, not a bench. A love seat! It is carved of precious ruby. It sits under the gentle shade of an ancient tree that thrives in love's garden. Come sit with me, beloved, as we let the whispers of the Great Beloved, come carried upon the sweet afternoon breeze, penetrate our hallowed ears.

The harvest will be at the best time, when the ripeness is just right, so utterly juicy and sweet. You shall know with certainty that this was the best way; not a moment sooner would have been as perfect, nor a moment later.

Her hair forms the galaxies, her thoughts become the stars. The sun is her own warmth and her breath is felt upon this earth, causing the roar of the ocean waves. Her voice is heard in the call of the whales and the trill of the birds. Nothing lies outside of her sphere of influence and power, compassion and grace. That includes you and your dreams, great and small.

It is best to participate in this life with much less certainty than the mind would have us believe is necessary for inner peace. Inner peace doesn't come with understanding, it comes with trusting.

Can we understand a star? Or a galaxy? Perhaps not—yet we can choose to trust in its beauty and beingness, and from it derive great energy, hope and inspiration.

*Follow your heart to discern the hidden mystery, where roses bloom
and streams of devotion flow.* — Rumi

Healing Process

FOR WHEN YOU REALLY NEED TO MANIFEST SOMETHING IMPOSSIBLE

SPIRITUAL GUIDANCE

The human heart knows everything envisioned can manifest according to divine timing and grace. Yet the mind does quake with fear, so much so that it will not listen to the heart at times. The mind holds itself captive with dark fantasies of that profound rejection and then avoids confronting it directly at all costs. It creates barriers instead, truly nothing more than lines in the sand believed to be forts.

But what strongholds – imaginary or real – can resist love's strength? It is like water. It seeps into every available space and changes form to survive in every environmental condition. It will erode blockages and prevail, no matter how long that process takes. It carves the earth into shape and form. Where it is, there is life, just like love.

So now you are guided to drop the doubt. Shed the incredulity and open the mind. You may not yet be consciously aware of what your own great heart desire is, but your heart holds the secret knowledge and will unveil it when your mind can handle it. Perhaps you have already caught a glimpse of your impossible dream and are ready to turn your previously created world upside down, and allow what could never be (or so you once believed), to be.

SACRED HONOURING RITUAL

Place your hands very lightly at your throat.

Say aloud: *With Rumi who loves me unconditionally as my witness, I now offer myself into the hands of the all-loving creative intelligence of this universe. I release all vows, intentions or beliefs ever made – consciously or unconsciously, in this or any lifetime – that are based in doubt and fear, holding me back from the creative fruition of my soul upon the earth. I dedicate myself to love and accept the gift of grace that brings me into greater fulfilment now. May I be blessed, so I can surrender resistance and accept what is coming to me now for what it is – a gift of love. So be it.*

Place your hands at your heart and focus on your breath for a moment or two as it flows in and out.

Write a list, if you wish, of impossible dreams that you would like to manifest. Say to the Universe: *You accomplish many impossible things in every moment. My cells elicit billions of processes every second. Bees fly even though their wings are too small for their bodies. Light is created from darkness. You can handle anything that I ask of you – so here is what I would like to manifest* … (share your impossible dreams with the Universe by speaking them aloud, from your heart now). *Thank you for your generosity and grace. I am open to being lovingly, clearly and mercifully guided to the fulfilment of these heart desires.*

When you are ready, place your hands in prayer and bow your head to your hands. You have completed your sacred honouring ritual.

No mine has a ruby like you! No world has a life like you, for this is the
diminishing world, and you are the expanding soul. — Rumi

Perhaps you have caught a sniff of the aromas from the divine kitchen and know the meal is nearly ready — and it smells delicious!

No matter whether things appear to be working out, they are.

You are held in the loving protection of the Divine Mother to keep you from straying from your highest path and divine destiny. There is work for you to do upon this planet, in your own unique way. It is the work of the Divine Mother, the work of love. So then, allow her to care for you, even if at times you wonder what the heavenly minx is up to!

Sometimes it is as though a greater hand smacks our wrist the moment we try to take firm hold of something, someone, anything, that brings us certainty or inner stability. Such are the rigours at an advanced stage on the path. We enter this place when we are ready for something wilder and more inspired than predictability.

Sometimes it might feel as though your fantasy is dying. It may be very painful and bring you much grief. But all that is dying is your attachment and opinion about how it must be. This needs to happen so you can stop dreaming it, and start living it.

Rise up now from your doubts and admonishments, and let your human self be loved.

Be kind to your heart. You may believe it to be weary from doubt and distrust, so much heartbreak and so many agonies, yet still it beats. Still it persists, with unquestioning allegiance to life. What a grand heart it is, this sacred heart of yours. How can it be worthy of anything other than tenderness, gratitude, acknowledgement and appreciation?

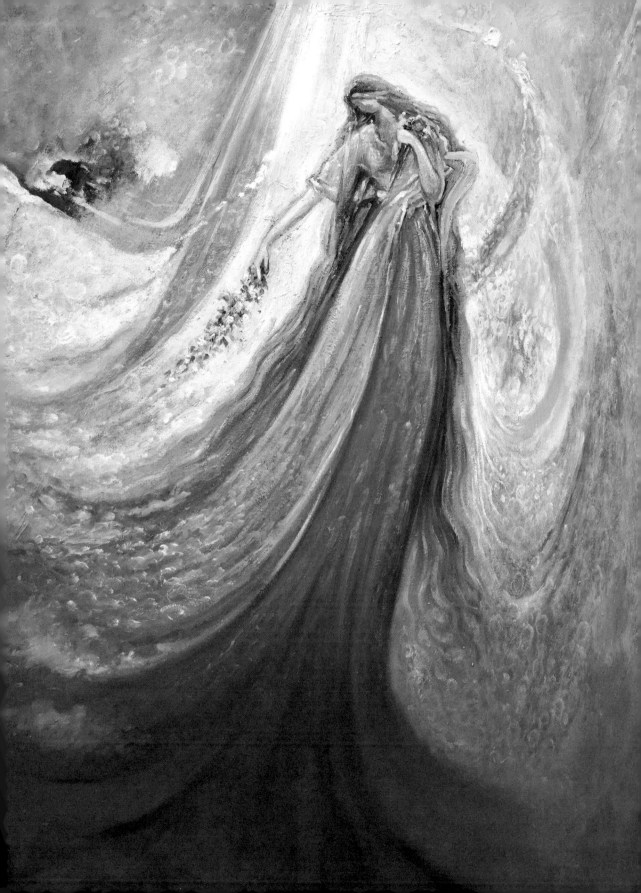

I have the perfect gift for you. It is a gown of new colours—of colours perfectly suited to you and no other. The colours of this gown will make your eyes sparkle and gleam as though they were more beautiful than the most precious of gems. So, hold on no longer to that shabby, tattered cloak, so unworthy of you. Cast it off! Let me grace your shoulders with this royal robe instead, that you may shine as beautifully as befits a royal child of divine parentage.

Do not allow yourself to be dragged into dramas or power games. You are worth so much more than that. Be in your dignity and power and keep going.

Allow the divine hand to reach for you. Do not let old shame, guilt or mistaken notions of false independence keep you from accepting this helping heavenly hand! This hand reaches to gently wipe away tears of the past. It will deftly unravel the ties that have bound your hands, preventing you from fully giving and receiving according to your worth which is incontestable and without limit.

A love letter from the Universe to your heart: How I adore your defiant, rebellious heart! It knows that what is an end for the mind, is for the heart, another match to ignite the sacred flames, which become holy fire from which it rises, again and again, like a glorious phoenix.

In you there is both the raging warrior who fights with unbreakable honour, and the healer who brings together those things torn apart.

A prayer honouring the mysterious qualities of light and dark within: I witness my darkness with compassion and become able to dance with all my being – light and dark – in graceful acknowledgement of my divine wholeness. The gentle acceptance of all of me now brings me peace.

Arrakis, dancing star of the heavens, incites our souls to feel the rhythm of life and surrender to it in flow, in grace, in clumsiness, and in play. Like a child who thinks not of the 'right steps' but just moves with music and with joy, she reminds you to dance freely and from your heart.

Your star mother keeps an eye on all the wild games happening in the sacred playground of the earth. No bully shall prevail over you. Be demanding in claiming her love for you. Be like the child wailing for its mother, "Ma! Ma! Ma! Come close!" Then she descends! A rampaging cosmic tigress rushes to protect her beloved cub. She will fight for you. Nothing can resist her light.

Without a doubt, happiness and joy are embedded in my heart! I am done with wishing, or with regret for having too little or too much! I AM FREE! — Rumi

Rassouli

HEART HEALING FOR YOUR PERFECT
AND HUNGRY DIVINE HEART

SPIRITUAL GUIDANCE

Even in its tremendous gratitude for all that is – and there is much gratitude and sweet appreciation in that precious heart of yours – there is a murmuring, a questing. It cries out to heaven: *"Vouchsafe me a blessing! I cannot go on! I am broken and in need of your tenderness for healing! I am empty and in need of filling, not with stuff and bits but with the most precious nectar of divine fulfilment! Nothing else will satisfy me!"*

There is a sense within you – perhaps quite obvious to your conscious mind, or perhaps only dimly registered as an unnameable underlying sense of anxiety. It is a sense that something in your life is not quite fulfilled. It may be the sense – even amongst so much gratitude – of a yearning yet to be met, a longing yet to be named and satisfied.

It is the pain, the real noble pain of the heart, that says: *"There is something more than this inadequacy, this settling for plastic instead of precious gemstones, that must end now. I cannot be fed by pixilated sunsets in animation upon my computer screen. I yearn to be blasted by so much radiance and beauty, by the real thing, that I become stupefied! I must witness so much divine splendour that all I can utter is some incoherent grunt, my mind disassembled and my heart ignited. Give me what I need most, even when I don't know how to explain it!"*

SACRED HONOURING RITUAL

Place one hand on your heart and one on your belly. Say the following aloud: *Rumi, who loves me unconditionally, guide me now, heal my heart. Guide me to the holy table where the true feast awaits. I am no longer satisfied by stale crumbs or the remnants of another's feast. With your mercy, grace and wisdom, guide me there, dearest brother of my soul. I cast my soul into your care and follow my nose! I follow my nose towards the sweetest scent of the banquet that has been prepared for my very own soul.*

Rest or stand up and dance your prayer. Just be with your body and how it wants to be — to rest or move now. Whatever you choose, stay with your breath and with what feels truthful. Let your heart guide you into authentic expression.

Say aloud: *I release that which is not worthy for my soul to feast upon. I do not decide this for myself from a place of distrust or judgment. I surrender my attachment and I trust in the sacred workings of life to present to me what is needed. In sacred trust, I surrender. My heart and soul and body and mind are to be completely nourished by divine nectar. So be it.*

You have finished your sacred honouring ritual.

When the grace of love is revealed, be a mirror to reflect it.
—— Rumi

You are the child, so secure in the love of the mother, that you trust in life implicitly and in what is brought to your door.

Is it difficult to see your magnificence? Without a mirror the size of a galaxy, how could you possibly witness all that you are? You are swathed in robes of grace, so light and freeing that they do not weigh you down, and yet so luscious and full that you cannot help but stir the movement of all of creation as you step this way and that.

Oh, what a spiritual marathon you have been running! Now the end is in sight.
You are drinking the sacred waters to replenish you from your journey.

Test your legs—you'll find them powerful and ready. Get set to fly! Test your wings—trust is one, daring is the other. You'll find them enthusiastic for flight and ready to learn to ride the currents, purpose-built for soaring to great heights.

With great blessings, great growth is possible. However, the blessings don't do the growth for us, making it magically happen. They give us the oomph we need, the power, the opportunities and the assistance we need, yet it is still we who take the journey.

Al-Uzza, the ancient shining one, also known as the Star of Venus, holds much power and strength. Even a small blessing of her light is more powerful than the fear of thousands, if not millions, of people. She is shining for your soul, now.

Angel Razbar shall show you the way, for she knows you from a long, long time ago, though you might have temporarily forgotten the acquaintance. She is a great hostess and guide in this terrain of divine love and she remembers you. You, who are great of heart and capable of contribution. You, who are now signing up for service in the great work of love.

Like a maturing adult who is ready to take on the mantle of a greater responsibility, your soul is stepping up. You are going through a process of assuming more spiritual responsibility for the honest and empowered expression of your own essence, and through that, your healing presence in the world is increasing.

You are making a positive impact in the world—more than you consciously realise.

On the path of love there is not so much wrong and right in the moral sense, so much as what is wrong or right for you. The mind cannot help so much here. Only the heart can recognise such truths.

It is said that one man's meat is another man's poison. Basing your choices on what others have chosen for themselves may damage your soul. Better to listen to the wisdom of your own heart.

There is somewhere you are meant to be. It is here, now, in this moment.

A prayer for the wisdom angel of the heart:
I give my heart permission to lead this dance. I give my mind some time
off – no more worry or doubt, planning or resisting. Instead, I surrender.
Instead, I open. Instead, I allow. And all unfolds with perfection, divine timing
and the miracle of grace. With Rumi as my soul witness, so be it.

Desire does not have to be a hindrance on the path. It can show us our passions and help us find our purpose. However, the belief it can only be sated in the way we think is best, can cause unnecessary confusion and suffering. Remain true to your desire, but be open to manifestation that surprises, astonishes and delights you.

Life operates according to a genius that is beyond a linear approach.
It is to be trusted rather than understood.

Are you aware that sweetness is found everywhere in this town?
— Rumi

When you enter the garden of the heart, you become fragrant like the rose.
— *Rumi*

Your soul is ready for Laylat al-Qadr, the Night of Destiny. Your ego counters, "Oh no, I have to wash my hair, and I have to sort through my accounts, and count my fingers and my toes. It will take me too long, and I simply won't be ready to attend. I am working long and hard at things so very important." Stick out your tongue, put on your dancing shoes, and go on your date with destiny.

Now is the time to gently, carefully, tend to the walls you once placed between yourself and life—walls of tentativeness, excessive caution, fear of abandonment and betrayal, doubt of your own lovableness, and doubts without substance based on past pain. You are so much greater than these crumbling walls. They are the stuff that is designed for demolition, not devotion and honouring.

This is the invitation to lay aside despair, to lay aside doubt in the capacity of the human heart—even your frustration and impatience. It is time to quit whipping yourself and others, no matter how noble the intention behind the whip may be, and start dancing instead.

It takes a great spirit, one with much practice of studied rebellion, to be ready to cast off the shackles of society from a place of loving defiance rather than fearful anger. And to playfully say to the world, "I have tasted your stale bread and underdeveloped wine. I decline your offer to gorge upon such lesser fruits. I prefer to feast upon bread, hot and fresh, and wine that is mouth-filling and sweet. Join me if you like. There is plenty for all."

You have divine permission to do something ridiculous—be it ridiculous in your own mind for your age or career path, or some identity or version of yourself you or another hold. The more ridiculous or inappropriate it seems—the more it moves you from your heart, without rhyme or reason—the better. This is not about hurting people or behaving without moral code. It is about letting your soul be free.

Sometimes you know something deep in your bones, without knowing how or why, or without particular reason. It may be joy that you know. It may be that you know to avoid a certain situation. It may be that something is going to work out beautifully, despite appearances to the contrary. It may be that you are meant to take a certain path. You just know.

The old wisdoms teach of cycles, of timing, of letting go to allow for new life to happen, and of the greater intelligence and scheme of life to which we must surrender if we are ever to know even a moment's peace.

Whatever is going on in your life right now — whether it brings you joy or deepest struggle — is the Divine in you, breaking through into your life. Do not hesitate to trust in it — embrace it fully and let it have its way.